Short Run SPC

Donald J. Wheeler

SPC Press, Inc.
Knoxville, Tennessee

SPC Press, Inc.
5908 Toole Drive
Knoxville, Tennessee 37919
(615) 584–5005
Fax (615) 588–9440

ISBN 0-945320-12-4

1 2 3 4 5 6 7 8 9 0

Contents

In September 1960, a new definition of World-Class Quality was quietly introduced...

"On-Target with Minimum Variance."

Operating "On-Target" requires a different way of thinking about our processes.

*Operating with "Minimum Variance" is achieved only when
a process displays a reasonable degree of statistical control.*

Both of these concepts are revolutionary.

Introduction

With today's emphasis upon both synchronous manufacturing and the reduction of in-process inventory, production runs are, in general, becoming shorter and shorter. As these efforts tend to tie the various steps in the production process more closely together, it becomes even more critical to predict just what will be produced, and when. Instead of being concerned with the delivery of 1500 parts a week, or 6000 parts once each month, now one may need 300 parts delivered at 10 a.m. every day of the week. In such an environment, predictability is everything, and uncontrolled variation can literally put one out of business.

Of course Shewhart provided us with an operational definition of when a production process will be predictable—it will be predictable only if it displays a reasonable degree of statistical control.

This lack of statistical control is what so often turns "just-in-time" into "already-too-late." Parts have to be helicoptered in, warehouses have to be built, and the costs of all this extra work has to be hidden somewhere. Toyota has proven that the just-in-time approach obviously works. The western imitators have also proven that there cannot be any real change, and the real savings of just-in-time cannot be achieved, without the predictability that is only available through statistical control.

For example, consider the problem of making a piece of interior trim for an automobile. The assembly plant would like for the trim pieces to come out of the shipping container in the build-order sequence (gray, tan, black, blue, red, etc.). The assembly plant asks the producer to load the containers in this manner. The idea is for the producer to program his production lines to make the trim pieces in the proper sequence, so that he can make the parts and directly load them into the shipping container. Sounds great. But what if the producer only has an 80% chance of making a usable part on any given cycle? All of his planning will be worthless. He will not be able to make the parts in a given sequence, since he cannot plan on making a given part at a given time. Every cycle is like a roll of the dice. He may or may not get a usable piece from that cycle. So what can this manufacturer do? He can only build a warehouse to inventory his parts, and ship to the assembly plant from this inventory. If a production process is out of control, or if it is not capable of meeting specifications, then shipping from inventory is the only way the manufacturer can participate in a just-in-time scheme. Planning production to fit in with the shipping schedule requires a production process which is in the Ideal State.

Thus, today even more than in the past, efficient operations place an emphasis upon that stability and predictability which only comes when a process is operating in the Ideal State. The four requirements for the Ideal State are:

1. The process must be inherently stable over time.

2. The manufacturer must operate the process in a stable and consistent manner. The operating conditions cannot be selected or changed arbitrarily.

3. The process aim must be set and maintained at the proper level.

4. The Natural Process Limits must fall within the specification limits.

These four requirements cannot be met without the use of control charts, yet the frequent changes required by the short production runs have made it hard for some to see how to apply the control charts. It is the purpose of this book to address the major problems that are created by frequent and deliberate process changes.

The list above begins with the job of establishing and maintaining process stability. This is made difficult by the frequent changeovers from one product to another. How do you visualize a stable production process when the process is being moved around? This issue is addressed in Part One.

Once a process has been stabilized, and it is operated in a stable and consistent manner, then one comes to the problem of setting the process aim correctly. Even a very stable process will make junk if the aim is far enough off target. Ways to use the data generated by a production process to check on deliberate adjustments of the process aim will be discussed in Part Two.

Finally, once a process is stabilized, and maintained in a state of statistical control, with the proper aim, it will be in the Ideal State only if it is capable—the Natural Process Limits are within the Specification Limits. When this fortuitous situation occurs, one can plan on producing the product in the proper order and shipping without having to inventory the product and handle it twice. While this whole procedure requires work, it does save time, reduce inventory, and increase the quality of the product and productivity of the plant.

The lazy way out is to build that warehouse, and hope that your competitor is doing the same. Of course, if he is not...

Part One

Tracking the Process

While Making Different Products

Control charts may be easily adapted to short production runs. The two main requirements for making these adaptations are (1) an appreciation of the fact that reasonable limits may be obtained from small amounts of data, and (2) an understanding of how to use control charts to discover new information rather than merely confirming what is already known. Part One of this book will discuss some of the ways that control charts may be modified to accommodate changes in a production process which are inherent or deliberate.

The adaptations given here include Difference Charts, Zed Charts, Charts for Mean Ranges, Zed-Star Charts, Difference Charts for subgrouped data, Zed-Bar Charts and Zed-Bar-Star Charts. Each of these charting techniques are illustrated with detailed examples. In addition to these seven techniques, a chapter is included outlining the role of the Moving Range Chart.

Chapter One

Difference Charts

Unit 11 is used to produce Products 1105 and 1108. In order to keep from building inventory, Unit 11 alternates between these two products, with short production runs for each. Every so often, a sample is taken from the production stream and its final characteristic is measured. These values are shown in time order in the following table.

Sample	Product	Value	Sample	Product	Value	Sample	Product	Value
11	1108	33	28	1105	22	45	1105	24
12	1108	37	29	1108	33	46	1105	23
13	1105	24	30	1108	36	47	1108	34
14	1108	35	31	1108	38	48	1108	34
15	1105	22	32	1105	22	49	1108	34
16	1105	23	33	1105	21	50	1105	21
17	1105	25	34	1105	23	51	1105	23
18	1105	23	35	1108	35	52	1108	34
19	1108	32	36	1105	26	53	1108	30
20	1108	34	37	1108	35	54	1105	22
21	1108	33	38	1105	24	55	1105	25
22	1108	37	39	1108	33	56	1108	35
23	1105	26	40	1105	21	57	1108	36
24	1108	36	41	1108	35	58	1108	37
25	1108	35	42	1105	27	59	1108	35
26	1105	23	43	1105	26	60	1105	25
27	1105	26	44	1105	25			

(The readings in the previous table could be the measurements on every k^{th} item coming down a conveyor belt, or they might be the test values for successive batches coming from a single reactor in a chemical process. There are many different situations which give rise to data similar to these.)

These data can be separated according to product and placed on control charts. Such charts may be called "Product Control Charts" since they each track one and only one product. The Product Control Charts for Products 1105 and 1108 are shown below.

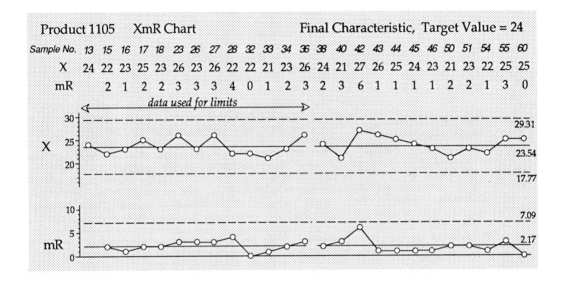

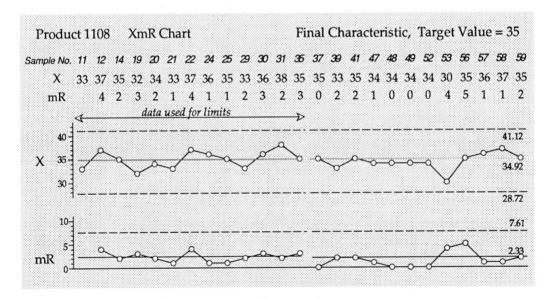

Figure 1: XmR Charts for Product 1105 and 1108

Product Control Charts provide a report card on each product. However, since they fragment the record of the production process they will be of little use to those who have to run the production process. Thus, production personnel will need a different way of charting these data before they will be able to to visualize the production process.

One rather simplistic approach to visualizing the production process is to simply plot the raw data in a running record. Of course the changes from one product to another will dominate such a running record, and little else besides these known changes will be seen on such a chart. If one should attempt to compute limits using all of the data the limits will be inappropriate for every product. On the other hand, if limits are fitted to each product separately the chart will be excessively messy.

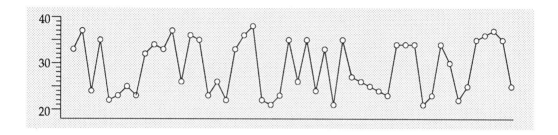

Figure 2: Running Record for Raw Data from Unit 11

The major swings shown on the running record for Unit 11 are the known changes between product 1105 to 1108. *Instead of reinforcing that which is already known, it is much better to use charts to discover that which is unknown.* Therefore, the known differences between Products 1105 and 1108 need to be removed from these data. This is done by subtracting the target value for each product from each of the measurements. The result will be a "Difference Chart."

Difference Charts will allow one to visualize the underlying production process even though it is used for short runs of different products.

Difference Charts for individual values are also known as "X-Nominal charts," and "X-Target charts." The "Nominal Value" which is subtracted from each observed value will be specific to each product, and may be either the historic grand average for each product, or a target value for each product. In either case, the central line for the Difference Chart is taken to be zero. The control limits for the Difference Chart are set at:

$$\text{Control Limits for X-Nominal Values} = 0.0 \pm 2.66 \, \overline{mR}$$

where the Average Moving Range, $\overline{mR}$, may be obtained from either the baseline data on the Product Control Charts or the moving ranges computed from the X–Nominal values. It is very important that one uses the preceding formula. Other measures of dispersion which might be available are completely inappropriate.[*]

A Moving Range Chart should be used in conjunction with the Difference Chart. The central line for this Moving Range Chart will be set equal to the Average Moving Range:

$$CL_R = \overline{mR}$$

and the upper control limit for these moving ranges will be:

$$UCL_R = 3.268\,\overline{mR}$$

The Difference Chart for Unit 11 is shown below, beginning with sample number 37.

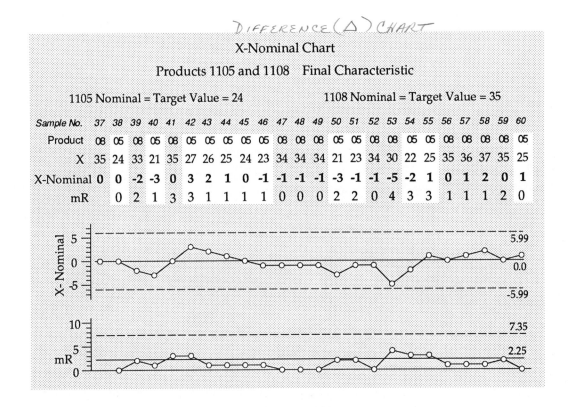

DIFFERENCE (Δ) CHART

X-Nominal Chart
Products 1105 and 1108   Final Characteristic

1105 Nominal = Target Value = 24   1108 Nominal = Target Value = 35

Sample No.	37	38	39	40	41	42	43	44	45	46	47	48	49	50	51	52	53	54	55	56	57	58	59	60
Product	08	05	08	05	08	05	05	05	05	05	08	08	08	05	05	08	08	05	05	08	08	08	08	05
X	35	24	33	21	35	27	26	25	24	23	34	34	34	21	23	34	30	22	25	35	36	37	35	25
X-Nominal	0	0	-2	-3	0	3	2	1	0	-1	-1	-1	-1	-3	-1	-1	-5	-2	1	0	1	2	0	1
mR		0	2	1	3	3	1	1	1	1	0	0	0	2	2	0	4	3	3	1	1	1	2	0

Figure 3: Difference Chart for Unit 11

---

[*] One must explicitly avoid the use of the *s* statistic in computing limits for individual values. It is always incorrect to compute control limits using a dispersion statistic which has been computed on a single pass through all the data.

When constructing a Difference Chart it is always better to first record the raw data and then to record the X–Nominal value. This provides a way to check any out-of-control point to see if the proper Nominal Value has been subtracted.

The moving ranges for a Difference Chart are computed without regard for the changes in product.

The purpose of a Difference Chart is to visualize the underlying process even though known changes in aim are being made. The purpose of the Moving Range Chart is to check on the appropriateness of the limits for the Difference Chart and to signal abrupt changes in the process.

Of course, the Difference Chart will make sense only if the variation is relatively constant from product to product. If the Average Range values on the various Product Control Charts are reasonably similar, then the formulas above will yield appropriate limits for the Difference Chart. If, however, the Average Ranges for the different products are dramatically different it will be better to use a Zed Chart rather than a Difference Chart. (The Chart for Mean Ranges provides a way of examining a set of Average Ranges for consistency. It will be described in the next chapter.)

Chapter Two

Charts for Mean Ranges

The chart for Mean Ranges is a special type of average chart. Given m Average Ranges, each of which is the average of k subgroup ranges, where all mk subgroups are the same size, n, then these m Average Ranges may be plotted against the following limits:

$$\text{UCL}_{\overline{R}} = \overline{\overline{R}} + \frac{H d_3 \overline{\overline{R}}}{d_2 \sqrt{k}}$$

$$\text{CL}_{\overline{R}} = \overline{\overline{R}}$$

$$\text{LCL}_{\overline{R}} = \overline{\overline{R}} - \frac{H d_3 \overline{\overline{R}}}{d_2 \sqrt{k}}$$

where the d_2 and d_3 values are those for subgroups of size n, the $\overline{\overline{R}}$ value is the average of the m Average Ranges, and the constant H depends upon m, according to the following table:

m	2	3	4	5	6	7	8 or more[*]
H	1.82	2.38	2.61	2.75	2.87	2.94	3.00

If any one of the m Average Ranges falls outside these limits, take this as evidence

---

[*] The use of the multiplier H is based upon the nature of the comparison being made by the Chart for Mean Ranges. This is a special chart, used with a finite number of Average Ranges. When a control chart is used to compare a small number of averages it will err in a conservative direction— that is, it will sooner fail to detect a signal than it will give a false signal. The usage of the H multipliers given above is intended only for those situations where the control chart is being used to make a one-shot comparison between m averages. In these situations the likelihood of a false alarm will still be reasonably small (theoretical value approximately 0.01), and the chart will be more sensitive to any signals which may be present.

that the Difference Chart is inadequate to properly display the process data, and use a Zed Chart instead of a Difference Chart.

The values for d_2 and d_3 are given in the following table.

n	2	3	4	5	6	7	8	9	10	20	30
d_2	1.128	1.693	2.059	2.326	2.534	2.704	2.847	2.970	3.078	3.735	4.086
d_3	0.8525	0.8884	0.8798	0.8641	0.8480	0.8332	0.8198	0.8078	0.7971	0.7287	0.6927

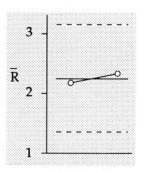

Using the data for Unit 11, there are $m = 2$ Average Ranges, each based upon $k = 12$ moving ranges, each of which were based upon $n = 2$ observations. These 2 Average Ranges are 2.17 and 2.33. The Overall Average Range is therefore:

$$\bar{\bar{R}} = 2.25$$

and the control limits for the Mean Range Chart are:

$$2.25 \ \pm \ \left[\frac{1.82\,(0.8525)\,2.25}{1.128\sqrt{12}} \right] = 1.36 \text{ to } 3.14.$$

Figure 4: Unit 11
Mean Range Chart

Since the Average Range values of 2.17 and 2.33 are both well within these limits the Difference Chart will be sufficient to plot the data from Unit 11. It will not be necessary to use a Zed Chart for the data from Unit 11.

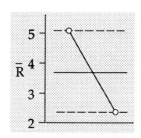

Using the data from Unit 12, which will be given in the following section, there are $m = 2$ Average Ranges, each based upon $k = 14$ moving ranges, each of which were based upon $n = 2$ observations. These 2 Average Ranges are 5.07 and 2.36. The Overall Average Range is therefore:

$$\bar{\bar{R}} = 3.71$$

and the control limits for the Mean Range Chart are:

Figure 5: Unit 12
Mean Range Chart

$$3.71 \ \pm \ \left[\frac{1.82\,(0.8525)\,3.71}{1.128\ \sqrt{14}} \right] = 2.35 \text{ to } 5.07.$$

Since the Average Range values of 5.07 and 2.36 are essentially equal to these limits, it is unlikely that Products 1201 and 1202 display the same amount of dispersion. Therefore, the Zed Chart will be better than a Difference Chart for the data from Unit 12.

Chapter Three

Zed Charts

The Zed Chart (also called a Z-Chart), makes allowances for different aim points at the same time that it makes allowances for different amounts of dispersion from product to product. In order to use a Zed Chart one will have to have both a Nominal Value and a Sigma(X) value[*] for each product. The Nominal Values may be either a target value or a grand average value. The Sigma(X) values will have to be obtained from the Product Control Charts. (Once again the reader is warned to avoid the use of the *s* statistic in obtaining a Sigma(X) value.) The observed value for a given product will be transformed into a Zed value by first subtracting off the Nominal Value for that product and then by dividing this difference by the appropriate Sigma(X) value for that product.

Unit 12 is used to produce Product 1201 and 1202. Product 1201 has an aim value of 19 for the final test value, while Product 1202 has an aim value of 8. The data for batches 43 through 72 are shown in the following table. The Product Control Charts, with limits based upon the data in the following table, are shown in Figures 6 and 7.

Batch	Product	Value	Batch	Product	Value	Batch	Product	Value
43	1201	20	53	1201	19	63	1201	23
44	1202	5	54	1202	7	64	1201	18
45	1201	25	55	1202	9	65	1202	9
46	1201	17	56	1201	18	66	1201	23
47	1201	21	57	1201	23	67	1202	9
48	1201	15	58	1201	18	68	1201	16
49	1202	9	59	1202	7	69	1202	8
50	1202	8	60	1202	7	70	1201	21
51	1202	12	61	1202	10	71	1202	12
52	1202	7	62	1201	15	72	1202	6

[*] The notation Sigma(X) is used here to denote any statistic which would, under appropriate theoretical conditions, be a *within-subgroup* estimator of the standard deviation parameter of a normal probability distribution. The formulas given in this section use one such statistic. Other statistics which yield *within-subgroup* estimators may also be used. If the reader is not familiar with the different types of estimators he should use the formulas given in this section.

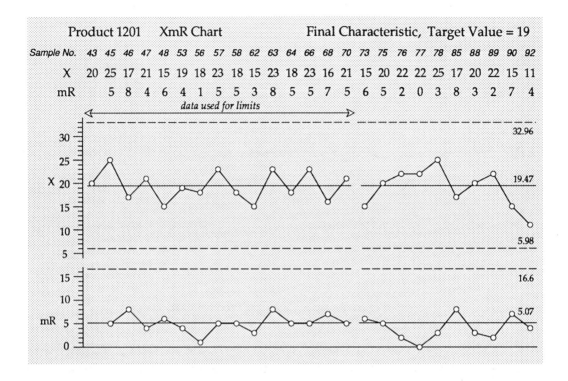

Figure 6: XmR Chart for Product 1201

Batches 43 through 70 for Product 1201 have an Average of 19.47, and an Average Moving Range of 5.07. Since the ranges are two-point moving ranges, the Average Range can be converted into standard deviation units by dividing by the d_2 value for $n = 2$: $d_2 = 1.128$.

$$\text{Sigma}(X) = \frac{\overline{R}}{d_2} = \frac{5.07}{1.128} = 4.49.$$

The observed value for a given product will be transformed by first subtracting the appropriate Nominal Value, and then this difference will be divided by the appropriate Sigma(X) value. The resulting value will be denoted by the symbol Z, and will be plotted on the Zed Chart.

For Product 1201, the target value of 19 will be used as the Nominal Value, and the the value for Sigma(X) will be the 4.49 computed above. Thus, for Product 1201, the Zed values will be obtained from the observed values by using the formula:

$$Z = \frac{X - 19}{4.49}$$

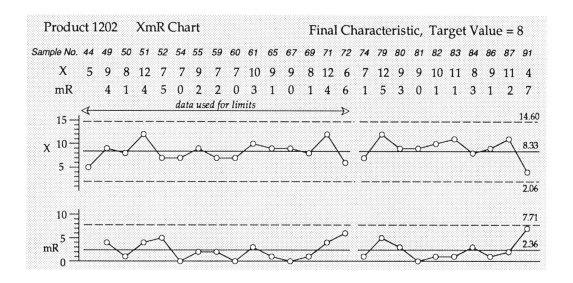

Figure 7: XmR Chart for Product 1202

The chart for Product 1202 has an Average of 8.33, and an Average Moving Range of 2.36 (based upon batches 44 through 72). Since the ranges are two-point moving ranges, the Average Range can again be converted into standard deviation units by dividing by d_2 = 1.128.

$$\text{Sigma(X)} = \frac{\overline{R}}{d_2} = \frac{2.36}{1.128} = 2.09.$$

For Product 1202, the target value of 8 will be used as the Nominal Value, and the 2.09 will be used as the Sigma(X) value. Thus, for Product 1202, the Zed values will be obtained using the formula:

$$Z = \frac{X-8}{2.09}$$

These Zed Values will be computed as appropriate for each observation obtained from Unit 12. They will then be plotted on a Zed Chart. The central line for the Zed Chart will be 0.0, and the limits will be placed at + 3.0 and – 3.0. A moving range should be computed using the Zed values. Traditionally this (standardized) range value has been denoted by the symbol W. These moving range values would be plotted on a W chart having a central line of d_2 = 1.128 and an upper control limit of:

$$\text{UCL}_W = d_2 + 3 d_3 = 3.686.$$

The Zed Chart for Unit 12 (Batches 73 through 92) is shown in Figure 8.

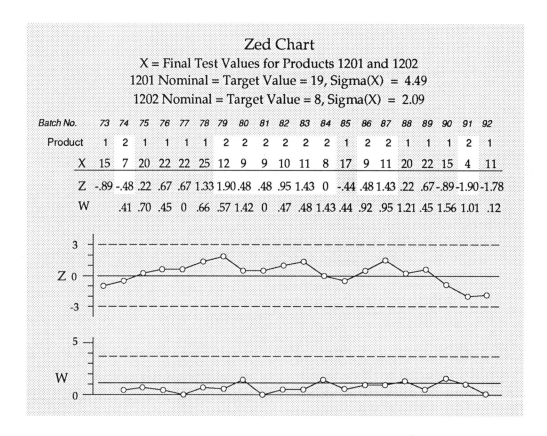

Figure 8: Zed Chart for Unit 12

In Figure 8 one may notice the long run above the central line beginning with Batch 75. This long run was not visible in Figures 6 and 7 because it was broken up between the two charts. Between Batch 75 and Batch 84 there was some special cause present which affected the aim of the process. If one uses this knowledge to discover the assignable cause, one will have discovered something about how to better operate this process. If one ignores this signal on the Zed Chart, then one will have missed an opportunity to have learned something about this process.

Z* Charts

A variation on the Zed chart is the Z* Chart. Instead of dividing by Sigma(X), the difference between the observed value and the Nominal value is divided by the appropriate Average Range:

$$Z^* = \frac{X - Nominal}{\bar{R}}$$

where both the Nominal value and the Average Range are defined for each separate product.

The Z* Chart has a central line of 0.0 and upper and lower control limits of ± 2.660.

The W* values are defined as two-point moving ranges for the Z* values. The central line for the W* values will be 1.0, and the upper control limit will be $D_4 = 3.268$.

Point by point the Zed Chart and the Z* Charts will look identical, but they will have different scales on the vertical axis. The user is free to choose either one. Just do not confuse the two charts because they do have different limits.

For reference, some of the Z* and W* values for Unit 12 (using Nominal values of 19 and 8 and Average Ranges of 5.07 and 2.36) are shown in the following table:

batch	73	74	75	76	77	78	79	80	81	82
product	1201	1202	1201	1201	1201	1201	1202	1202	1202	1202
X	15	7	20	22	22	25	12	9	9	10
Z*	-0.79	-0.43	0.20	0.59	0.59	1.18	1.68	0.43	0.43	0.84
W*		0.36	0.63	0.39	0.0	0.59	0.50	1.25	0.0	0.41

These Z* and W* values are all slightly smaller than the original Z and W values given in Figure 8.

Chapter Four

The Role of the Moving Range Charts

Both the Difference Chart and the Zed Chart have a Moving Range Chart included. While some have discounted the role of Moving Range Charts, these charts can provide useful information and should always be included. With Difference Charts and Zed Charts the moving range charts provide two checks on the procedure. First, a moving range which exceeds the upper control limit will indicate a probable shift in the production process. With Difference Charts and Zed Charts this may be due to an improper adjustment, or due to some unknown assignable cause. In either case, one will need to know about and to react to such changes.

Secondly, while runs on a moving range chart cannot be interpreted in the same way that runs on other charts are interpreted, one should still look to see if the moving ranges appear to be reasonably well centered on the chart. If, over a sustained period of time, the moving ranges tend to be mostly above the central line, or mostly below the central line, then it is likely that the initial Average Range values used to establish the chart were, respectively, too small or too large. In other words, since one may be constrained to establish limits using only a small amount of data, it is wise to use the Moving Range Chart to check on the appropriateness of the initial computations.

Since moving ranges can have artificial runs about the central line one will need to be very conservative in applying this check. However, if 15 to 20 successive values are all above or all below the central line, or if the running record for 30 or more moving ranges is noticeably off-center relative to the central line, then one should update the Difference Charts or the Zed Charts. The procedures for doing this will be illustrated using the data for Units 11 and 12. In both cases there is not quite enough evidence available to completely justify the following procedures.

The Moving Range Chart in Figure 3 has only 5 of the 23 moving ranges above the central line. This is an indication that the Average Ranges obtained from Figure 1 may be too large. If this type of behavior persists then it will be advisable to revise the limits for both the Difference Chart and its Moving Range Chart. Such a revision would use the moving ranges computed directly from the X–Nominal values instead of the values found on the Product Control Charts.

While the Average Ranges from the Product Control Charts will usually be appropriate for use in computing the limits for either the Difference Charts or the Zed Charts, they will occasionally be inflated. This inflation can occur due to the fact that some of the moving ranges on the Product Control Charts will represent longer time intervals than other moving ranges: that is, some moving ranges will be computed using values which did not occur consecutively in time. If the process is slowly drifting, these longer-term moving range values can be inflated. If they are inflated, the Average Ranges will also be inflated, and this inflation will be seen on the Moving Range Chart based upon the X–Nominal values or the Zed values.

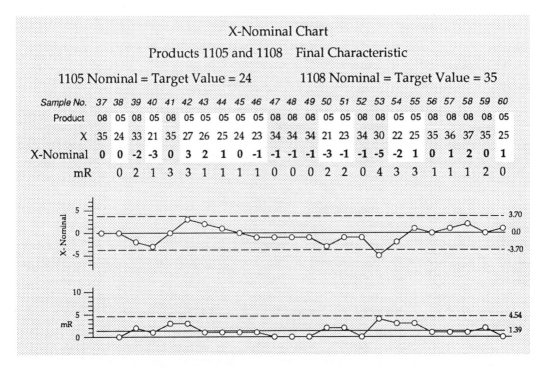

Figure 9: Difference Chart for Unit 11 with Revised Limits

Using the 23 moving ranges in Figure 3 to revise the limits for the Difference Charts for Unit 11 one gets the following:

$$\bar{R} = 1.39$$
$$UCL_R = 4.54$$

Control Limits for X–Nominal values = $0.0 \pm 2.66 (1.39) = -3.70$ to 3.70

The revised Difference Chart is shown in Figure 9. While the moving ranges now appear to be centered relative to their central line, Sample 53 is found to fall below the lower control limit on the Difference Chart.

When the moving ranges persist in being either too small or too large, one is justified in revising the limits.

The Moving Ranges based upon the Zed values in Figure 8 also appear to not be centered upon the central line. Only 4 out of the 19 moving ranges fall above the central line of 1.128. If such a pattern persisted in future observations, then one would eventually be justified in revising the computations for the Zed Charts. The operations for such a revision will be illustrated here even though in practice this author would wait for more evidence.

Moving ranges which are consistently smaller than the central line will indicate that the Sigma(X) values used in computing the Zed values were too large. (Division by inflated values will shrink the Zed values excessively, resulting in small moving ranges.) Thus, one should consider deflating the Sigma(X) values.

To compute the deflation factor for the Sigma(X) values begin by computing an average value for W. Divide this value by $d_2 = 1.128$, and deflate each of the Sigma(X) values by this proportion.

The W values for the Unit 12 data are found in Figure 8. They give the following:

$$\frac{\overline{W}}{d_2} = \frac{0.69}{1.128} = 0.618$$

Thus, the average of these nineteen moving ranges, $\overline{W}$, is only 61.8% as big as the expected central line value of 1.128. To compensate for this we deflate each Sigma(X) by multiplying by 0.618:

Product 1201: Sigma(X) = 0.618 (4.49) = 2.78
Product 1202: Sigma(X) = 0.618 (2.09) = 1.29

When these deflated Sigma(X) values are used to compute the Zed values one obtains the Zed Charts shown in Figure 10.

This deflation has centered the moving ranges relative to their central line, and it has changed the Zed values enough that two values now fall outside the control limits. While the long run signalled a lack of control for this process, these out-of-control points provide additional information about the presence of assignable causes.

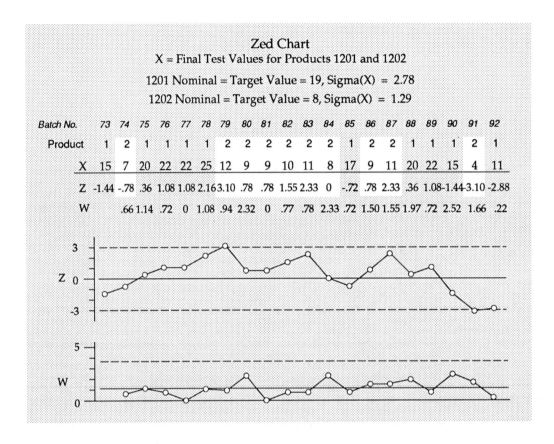

Figure 10: Revised Zed Charts for Unit 12

Notice that the effect of deflating the dispersion is the same on both the Difference Charts and the Zed Charts—more variation is visible on the chart for individual values when the dispersion is adjusted downward. With the Difference Charts the limits moved closer to the zero lines, while on the Zed Charts the limits remained fixed as the points moved further away from 0.

If the initial measures of dispersion were too small, and one adjusted them upward, then the effect upon the Difference and Zed Charts would be the opposite—less variation would be seen on these charts. This sensitivity of these control charts to the measures of dispersion used is not excessive as long as the limits or the transformations are based upon the proper dispersion statistics.

The purpose of the Difference Charts and the Zed Charts is the visualization of the underlying process even when the process is being deliberately changed. Both of these charts should always be used with a Moving Range Chart.

Chapter Five

Difference Charts for Subgrouped Data

With short production runs it seems somewhat inconsistent to think of subgrouping the limited data available. (When data are subgrouped there is an implicit assumption that the values within the subgroup are essentially homogeneous, and that no useful information is lost by averaging them together.) When groups of several consecutive parts are collected at specified intervals of time, then subgrouping makes sense. If however, one is only going to make, say, 50 items of a given type, and is going to measure 5 of these items, then it seems much more reasonable to select the first item and every tenth item thereafter instead of grabbing five consecutive items at one time. Furthermore, subgrouping these five measurements will make the control chart a mere report card—the point will be plotted after all of the items have been made. In contrast to this, plotting each individual value as it is obtained will let the user visualize the production process right from the start.

For these reasons, this author does not generally recommend using subgrouped data with short production runs. However, in case one has data which logically belong in subgroups, the appropriate procedures will be shown here. Difference Charts will be illustrated in this chapter, and the Zed-Bar Chart will be defined in Chapter Six.

Difference Charts for Subgrouped Data

Subgroup Averages may be converted into Differences by subtracting off an appropriate Nominal Value from each Subgroup Average. The Subgroup Ranges will be left unchanged. The observed data should always be recorded, along with the Subgroup Average and Subgroup Range, before the Difference is recorded.

The Difference Values, $(\overline{X} - \text{Nominal})$, and Subgroup Ranges, R, will be plotted against the following limits:

The Central Line for the Difference Values is set at 0.0

The Control Limits for the Difference Values are: $\pm A_2 \bar{\bar{R}}$

The Central Line for Subgroup Ranges is: $\bar{\bar{R}}$

The Control Limits for Subgroup Ranges are: $D_3 \bar{\bar{R}}$ and $D_4 \bar{\bar{R}}$

where $\bar{\bar{R}}$ is the Overall Average Range for all products produced by this process. Of course the Difference Chart is appropriate only when the variation is essentially the same for all products produced by the process. The Chart for Mean Ranges may again be used to check for this condition. If some of the products have excessive variation, then a Zed-Bar Chart will be needed instead of a Difference Chart for Averages.

Unit 13 makes Product 1311 and 1302. Once each hour a sample of three parts is obtained from the production line. The part number is noted and the parts are measured. These three measurements are then subgrouped and placed on a control chart. The Product Control Charts for 1311 and 1302 are shown in Figures 11 and 12.

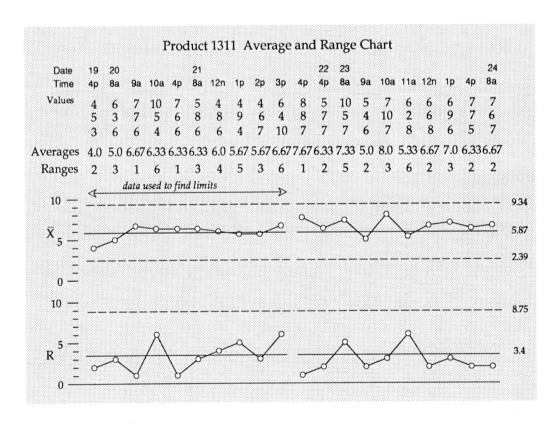

Figure 11: Average and Range Chart for Product 1311

The first ten subgroups in Figure 11 have a Grand Average of 5.867, and an Average Range of 3.4. The upper control limit for the subgroup averages is 9.34, and the lower control limit for the subgroup averages is 2.39. The upper control limit for the subgroup ranges is 8.75. The target value for this dimension of Product 1311 is 6.0. As in the other examples, this Product Control Chart provides a record of the production consistency for this one product, but it does not provide a useful window for viewing the production process.

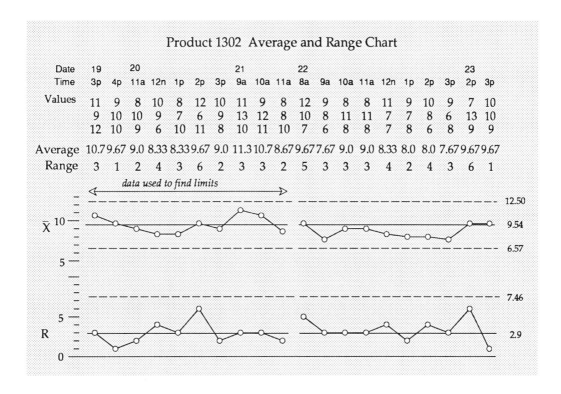

Figure 12: Average and Range Chart for Product 1302

The first ten subgroups in Figure 12 have a Grand Average of 9.535, and an Average Range of 2.9 The upper control limit for the subgroup averages is 12.50, and the lower control limit for the subgroup averages is 6.57. The upper control limit for the subgroup ranges is 7.46. The target value for this dimension of Product 1302 is 9.0.

The similarity of the Average Ranges will justify the use of a Difference Chart for these data (a Mean Range Chart could be used to check for detectably different Average Ranges). When the Average Ranges are similar, all that is needed is to accommodate the changes in aim. This is accomplished by subtracting off the target value from each Subgroup Average. The central line for these Difference Values will be 0.0. The control limits will be placed at:

$$\pm A_2 \overline{\overline{R}} = \pm 1.023\,(3.15) = \pm 3.22$$

where the Overall Average Range, $\overline{\overline{R}} = 3.15$, is the average of the subgroup ranges for both products. The central line for the Range Chart will be the Overall Average Range, and the upper control limit for the Range Chart will be:

$$D_4 \overline{\overline{R}} = 2.574\,(3.15) = 8.1$$

The Difference Chart for Unit 13 is shown in Figure 13. Notice how this chart shows the process sequentially in time. Each hour's sample is shown in order, so that one can visualize the behavior of the process with this chart. None of the runs are long enough to indicate a lack of control, and no points fall outside the control limits. Thus there is no evidence of assignable causes during this two day period.

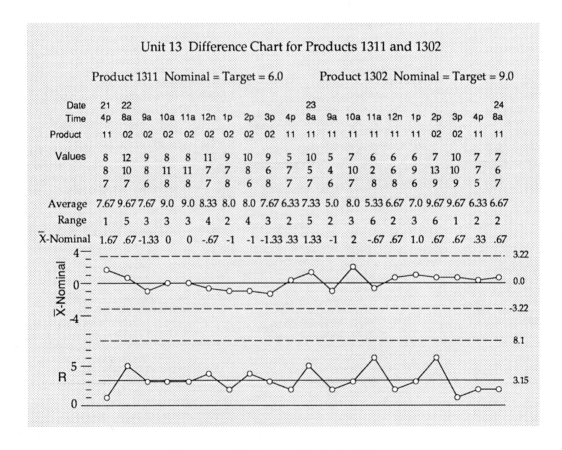

Figure 13: Difference Chart for Unit 13

The Range Chart will show when a single subgroup has excessive variation, but it may be difficult to spot a drift in the variation for a single product with this chart. This is why separate Product Control Charts are useful. If the limits on the Product Control Charts are based upon the target value and the Overall Average Range, then a product-specific drift in dispersion or location can be spotted more readily than such could be found on the Difference Chart.

Chapter Six

Standardized Charts for Subgrouped Data

The Zed-Bar Chart differs from the Zed Chart enough that the different name is helpful in avoiding confusion. In order to convert the Subgroup Averages and Subgroup Ranges into Zed-Bar and W values one will need:

> (1) a Nominal Value for each product,
>
> (2) a Sigma($\bar{X}$) value for each product,[*] and
>
> (3) a Sigma(X) value for each product.

Given these three quantities for each product, the Subgroup Averages are converted into Zed-Bar values according to the following formula:

$$\bar{Z} = \frac{\bar{X} - \text{Nominal}}{\text{Sigma}(\bar{X})}$$

where Sigma($\bar{X}$) will usually be found using:

$$\text{Sigma}(\bar{X}) = \frac{\bar{R}}{d_2 \sqrt{n}}$$

and the Subgroup Ranges are converted into W values according to the formula:

$$W = \frac{R}{\text{Sigma}(X)} .$$

The $\bar{Z}$ values will have a central line of 0.0, and control limits of ±3.0. The W

---

[*] The notation Sigma($\bar{X}$) denotes any statistic which would, under appropriate theoretical conditions, be a *within-subgroup* estimator of the standard deviation parameter of the sampling distribution of

values will have a central line at d_2 and control limits at $d_2 \pm 3\,d_3$, where d_2 and d_3 are determined by the subgroup size.

Unit 14 produces Products 1404, 1407 and 1408. Since the minimum length production run is eight hours, each run is simply identified by date of production. A total of five readings on the product are made during each day's run, and these five readings are subgrouped on the control chart.[*]

The target for Product 1404 is 4.5. The Average Range for ten subgroups of product 1404 is 4.10. Thus, the necessary values for finding the Zed-Bar and W values for Product 1404 will be:

$$\text{Nominal Value} = 4.5$$
$$\text{Sigma}(\bar{X}) = \frac{4.10}{2.326\sqrt{5}} = 0.788$$
$$\text{Sigma}(X) = \frac{4.10}{2.326} = 1.76$$

The target for Product 1407 is 9.5. The Average Range for ten subgroups of Product 1407 is 10.5. Thus, the necessary values for finding the Zed-Bar and W values for Product 1407 will be:

$$\text{Nominal Value} = 9.5$$
$$\text{Sigma}(\bar{X}) = \frac{10.5}{2.326\sqrt{5}} = 2.02$$
$$\text{Sigma}(X) = \frac{10.5}{2.326} = 4.51$$

The target for Product 1408 is 8.5. The Average Range for ten subgroups of Product 1408 is 7.9. Thus, the necessary values for finding the Zed-Bar and W values for Product 1408 will be:

$$\text{Nominal Value} = 8.5$$
$$\text{Sigma}(\bar{X}) = \frac{7.9}{2.326\sqrt{5}} = 1.52$$
$$\text{Sigma}(X) = \frac{7.9}{2.326} = 3.40$$

The Zed-Bar Chart for Unit 14 is shown in Figure 14.

---

the subgroup averages.

[*] Since these readings are spread out over time this subgrouping may be obscuring certain process behaviors. Data which are obtained periodically should not be subgrouped until after the data have been examined on an individuals chart. Here the data are left in subgroups for the sake of the example.

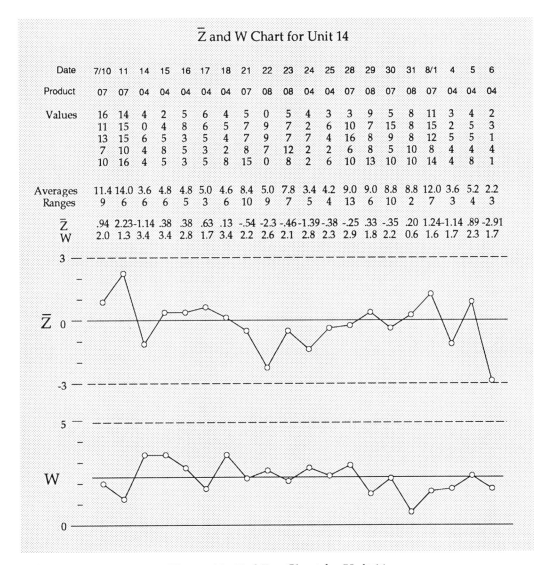

Z̄ and W Chart for Unit 14

Date	7/10	11	14	15	16	17	18	21	22	23	24	25	28	29	30	31	8/1	4	5	6
Product	07	07	04	04	04	04	04	07	08	08	04	04	07	08	07	08	07	04	04	04
Values	16	14	4	2	5	6	4	5	0	5	4	3	3	9	5	8	11	3	4	2
	11	15	0	4	8	6	5	7	9	7	2	6	10	7	15	8	15	2	5	3
	13	15	6	5	3	5	4	7	9	7	7	4	16	8	9	8	12	5	5	1
	7	10	4	8	5	3	2	8	7	12	2	2	6	8	5	10	8	4	4	4
	10	16	4	5	3	5	8	15	0	8	2	6	10	13	10	10	14	4	8	1
Averages	11.4	14.0	3.6	4.8	4.8	5.0	4.6	8.4	5.0	7.8	3.4	4.2	9.0	9.0	8.8	8.8	12.0	3.6	5.2	2.2
Ranges	9	6	6	6	5	3	6	10	9	7	5	4	13	6	10	2	7	3	4	3
$\bar{Z}$	.94	2.23	-1.14	.38	.38	.63	.13	-.54	-2.3	-.46	-1.39	-.38	-.25	.33	-.35	.20	1.24	-1.14	.89	-2.91
W	2.0	1.3	3.4	3.4	2.8	1.7	3.4	2.2	2.6	2.1	2.8	2.3	2.9	1.8	2.2	0.6	1.6	1.7	2.3	1.7

Figure 14: Zed-Bar Chart for Unit 14

Notice that the observed values, the original subgroup averages and the original subgroup ranges are recorded and then these values are transformed into Zed-Bar and W values. This provides the information necessary to check on the correctness of any given computation.

The fact that the formula for $\bar{Z}$ has a different divisor from the formula for W is a source of error that one must be careful about. One way of avoiding this source of confusion is to use a modified form of the Zed-Bar Chart: The Zed-Bar-Star Chart.

$\bar{Z}*$ Charts

Just as the Z* Chart was a simplification of the Zed Chart, the $\bar{Z}*$ Chart is a simplification of the regular Zed-Bar Chart illustrated above. Instead of dividing the Differences and Subgroup Ranges by appropriate Sigma values, both are divided by the appropriate Average Range value:

$$\bar{Z}* = \frac{\bar{X} - \text{Nominal}}{\bar{R}}$$

which has a central line of 0.0 and control limits of $\pm$ A_2, and

$$W* = \frac{R}{\bar{R}}$$

which has a central line of 1.0 and control limits of D_3 and D_4. (Remember that both the Nominal Value and the Average Range value will change from product to product.)

Point by point these charts will look like the charts in Figure 14. By changing the labels on the vertical scale the same picture could be used for both charts.

Chapter Seven

Recommendations

Whenever the amount of data is limited one should begin with Charts for Individual Values, Difference Charts for Individual Values, and Zed Charts. Charts for Mean Ranges may be used to see if a Zed Chart is needed. Always include a Moving Range Chart with these charts for individual values.

Whenever the data are collected periodically one should always begin with charts for individual values. If the process tends to change slowly relative to the sample frequency, then such data may be subgrouped in appropriate ways with little loss of information.

If the data are obtained in clusters, the subgrouping of these data and the use of Difference Charts for Subgrouped Data and Zed-Bar Charts may be appropriate. If the chart is to be used by those running the process one should be careful to avoid subgrouping too much data together. With large subgroup sizes, or a low subgroup frequency, short production runs can result in control charts that are nothing but ancient history. With short production runs it is often better to measure fewer parts more frequently, and to use charts for individual values, than it is to subgroup the data.

Finally, the Difference Chart and the Zed Chart may be used when the process is changing in a known manner, such as drift due to tool wear, clogging, or deactivation of a catalyst. In such situations, where there is a known and definite change in the process average as a function of time, the Nominal Value may be made into a function of time. When this is done, the amount subtracted would depend upon the time period. This approach will accommodate both linear and non-linear drifts. While doing this may be slightly complicated, it is much simpler than any alternative method that may be used, and it will provide a graph that may be used in real-time decisions.

Part Two

Setting the Process Aim

With shorter and shorter production runs the ability to set up a run so that it will operate on-target may make the difference between success and failure. Without a bank of in-process inventory to cushion the impact, and without adequate lead time to allow for reworking or re-fabricating the product, a single faulty run can close down a whole assembly operation. Thus, it becomes even more critical to set-up each run properly. Some ways to use the data generated by the process to assess the process aim will be described here in Part Two. While these procedures will be especially useful with short production runs, they may be used in virtually any manufacturing environment.

Chapter Eight

The Difference Between Aim and Consistency

The following example shows three processes. Two processes of these processes have great consistency, yet are not meeting the specifications because of poor process aim. The third process has neither good consistency nor good aim.

Example: *Length of Connecting Wires:*

The control chart shown in Figure 15 was made by a reliability engineer who was investigating a problem with the length of a connecting wire. The wires were purchased from three different suppliers, and were supposed to be 100 mm long, with a specified tolerance of ± 4 mm.

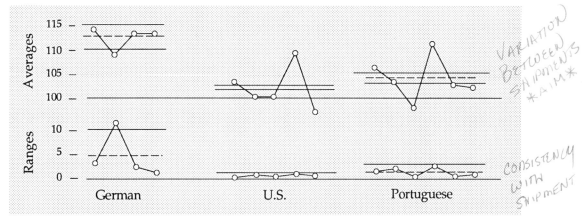

Figure 15: Control Charts for Connecting Wire Lengths

The data for each subgroup consist of the lengths of five pieces of wire. Each subgroup represents exactly one shipment.

The four shipments from the German supplier had a Grand Average of 112.7 mm and an Average Range of 4.6 mm. Although there were only four subgroups, there is a detectable lack of control on both the Average Chart and the Range Chart.

The five shipments from the U.S. supplier had a Grand Average of 102.2 mm and an Average Range of 0.6 mm. Here, the Average Chart is so completely out of control that none of the subgroup averages are within the control limits.

The six shipments from the Portuguese supplier had a Grand Average of 104.0 mm and an Average Range of 1.4 mm. Once again, the Average Chart is badly out of control.

So what was to be done? The U.S. and Portuguese suppliers showed great consistency within shipments, but a total lack of consistency between shipments. The German supplier showed very poor consistency within each shipment, and a lack of consistency between shipments.

Since the wires from all suppliers were out of control, the engineer decided to consider whether they might all be able to improve their products. The Hypothetical Process Spread for the U.S. supplier was about 1.6 mm. For the Portuguese supplier, it was about 3.6 mm, and for the German supplier, it was about 5.9 mm. Based on this analysis, the plant stopped buying from the German supplier, and the other two suppliers were told that while they had great consistency within each shipment, they needed to improve the quality of their product by consistently setting their process aim at 100 mm.

Dr. Taguchi's notion of a Quadratic Loss Function leads directly to the result that operating on-target with minimum variance will always minimize the costs due to variation from target. A rigorous treatment is not required—one does not need to know precisely the actual shape of the loss function, nor does one need to know the distribution for product characteristic. As long as the loss function is minimum at the target, non-negative, and piecewise smooth, the minimum average loss per unit of production will occur when the process is operating on-target with minimum variance. Thus, in addition to operating with a reasonable degree of statistical control, one must know how to get the process on-target.

For the sake of clarity, the following nomenclature will be used throughout Part Two. The "process aim" denotes that value or values at which the adjustable process controls are set. Thus, the process aim represents all that is directly manipulated by the operator as he is making his adjustments. The "process average" is the average value of some product characteristic, averaged over all the product produced at a given process aim. The "target" is the desired value for the process average.

In the preceding example, the target value was 100 mm. The average for each subgroup approximates the process average for a given run (each shipment), and the process aim would consist of those controls over the fabrication of the connecting wires which the operator can manipulate.

An easy way to distinguish between these three quantities is given by the following: the "process aim" is what you set, the "process average" is what you get, and the "target" is what you want. Using this nomenclature, the objective of a set-up procedure is to adjust the process aim until the process average is close enough to the target to result in a satisfactory production run.

Why settle for close enough? Why not make the process average equal to the target? Simply because in practice, one must **estimate** the process average with an average, and averages are always subject to sampling variation. This guarantees that no procedure will ever be able to consistently make the process average exactly equal to the target. The best that can ever be achieved in practice is to get the process average close to the target most of the time. In order to do this, the procedure must use an adequate amount of data in conjunction with the proper decision rule or rules. (An inadequate amount of data can be worse than guessing, and the wrong decision rules will waste effort through an excessive number of wrong decisions.)

Thus, the problem of setting the process aim is one of using both the right amount of information and the right decision rules for interpreting that information. The following sections will detail several techniques for setting the process aim. Some of these techniques will use control charts, while others will use a separate data collection procedure.

PROCESS AIM WHAT YOU SET

PROCESS AVG IS WHAT YOU GET

TARGET IS WHAT YOU WANT

Chapter Nine

Setting the Process Aim
Using a Sequence of Values

The nature of the problem of setting the process aim is slightly different from the usual problem connected with a control chart. In general, an out-of-control signal indicates the presence of an assignable cause. Since one does not want to react to false alarms, the control chart is set up to avoid false alarms. However, when one has definitely and deliberately changed the process aim, the question is not whether there is an assignable cause present, but whether or not the change has had the desired effect.

Since it is always easier to obtain a contradiction than a confirmation, we shall assume that the change in the process aim had the desired effect—so that the process average is in the neighborhood of the target value—and then look for evidence that might contradict this assumption. To do this we shall use a chart for Individual Values.

Say that the process aim has been adjusted and the process is now stabilized at the new level. Periodically a sample is obtained from the product stream and measured. This single measurement can be placed on a special chart for Individual Values and used to judge if the process average is detectably off target.

This special chart for Individual Values will have the following features:

1. The central line for the X chart will be set at the target value.

2. A historic Sigma(X) value for Individual Values will be used to establish the three-sigma limits on either side of this central line.

3. One-sigma and two-sigma lines will be drawn, centered on the central line, on both sides of the chart for Individual Values.

4. Individual Values will be obtained and plotted on this X chart.

5. As each point is plotted, Detection Rules I, II, III, IV will be used to examine the data for a lack of control. Detection Rule I indicates a lack of control when a single point falls outside one of the three-sigma limits. Detection Rule II indicates a lack of control whenever at least two out of three successive values are beyond one of the two-sigma lines and on the same side of the central line. Detection Rule III indicates a lack of control whenever at least four out of five successive values are beyond one of the one-sigma lines and on the same side of the central line. Detection Rule IV indicates a lack of control whenever eight successive values fall on the same side of the central line.

6. Any lack of control on the Individual Chart will represent an off-target process. When a lack of control is detected, the average of the observations will provide a reasonable estimate of where the process average is located relative to the target, and the process aim should be adjusted accordingly. Following each adjustment, additional data are collected and analyzed to see if the process average is still detectably different from the target.

7. When 10 successive measurements fail to indicate a lack of control, using all four detection rules, the process average may be said to be reasonably close to the target. At this point one may shift from the "aim setting mode" back to a "monitoring mode" where the control chart tracks the process for potential upsets.

Since this is a procedure for setting the process aim, we will naturally be concerned primarily with the Individuals Chart. One can also compute the moving Ranges and plot them on a moving Range Chart, but this chart will only be of secondary interest in this case. The upper control limit for the moving Ranges would be:

$$[d_2 + 3\,d_3]\,\text{Sigma}(X) = 3.686\,\text{Sigma}\,(X),$$

while the central line for the moving Ranges would be:

$$d_2\,\text{Sigma}(X) = 1.128\,\text{Sigma}(X).$$

Example: *Setting the Process Aim With An XmR Chart:*

Product 15F is made on Unit 15. The target value for Product 15F is 9.0 units.
A control chart for Product 15F has shown a Sigma(X) value of 1.84 units.
Therefore, an Individual Chart is set up with the following lines:

$$UNPL_X = 9.0 + 3\,(1.84) = 14.52$$
$$upper\ 2\text{-}sigma\ line = 9.0 + 2\,(1.84) = 12.68$$
$$upper\ 1\text{-}sigma\ line = 9.0 + 1.84 = 10.84$$
$$Central\ Line = Target\ Value = 9.0$$
$$lower\ 1\text{-}sigma\ line = 9.0 - 1.84 = 7.16$$
$$lower\ 2\text{-}sigma\ line = 9.0 - 2(1..84) = 5.32$$
$$LNPL_X = 9.0 - 3(1.84) = 3.48$$

And a moving Range chart is set up with the following limits:

$$UCL_R = 3.686\,(1.84) = 6.78$$
$$CL_R = 1.128\,(1.84) = 2.08$$

After the process aim has been adjusted to hopefully achieve a process average near the target value of 9.0, data are collected and plotted on the XmR chart.

The first value is 11.

This value does not, by itself, suggest that the process average is off-target.

Therefore, no action will be taken at this point.

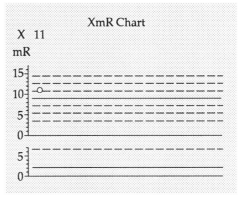

Figure 16: Setting the Process Aim

The next measured value is 16.

This value signals the need to further adjust the process aim.

The combined average of the values collected at this setting will suggest the magnitude of the needed adjustment.

This average is:

$$\frac{(11+16)}{2} = 13.5 .$$

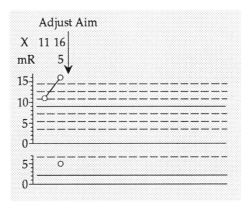

Figure 17: Setting the Process Aim

The Process Aim is adjusted downward by an amount which is thought to be about 4 units.

Following this adjustment the next value is 8.

This value is plotted on the chart.

At this time the chart does not indicate the need for further adjustment.

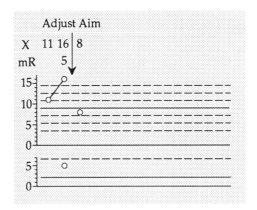

Figure 18: Setting the Process Aim

The next value is 11.

This value is plotted on the chart.

The value of 11, by itself or in conjunction with the previous value of 8, does not indicate a need for further adjustment.

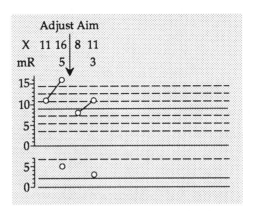

Figure 19: Setting the Process Aim

The next value is 8.

This value is plotted on the chart.

The values obtained since the last adjustment do not suggest a need for further adjustment.

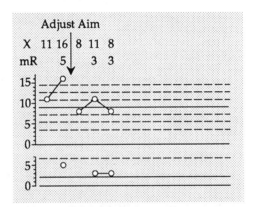

Figure 20: Setting the Process Aim

The next seven values are:
11, 6, 9, 8, 9, 10, and 9.

These values do not suggest a need for further adjustment.

Since a total of ten values have failed to detect a need for an adjustment, consider the process aim to be set sufficiently close to the target for a satisfactory production run.

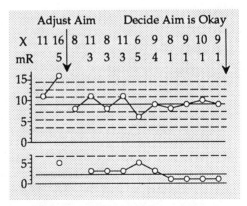

Figure 21: Setting the Process Aim

Before tampering with the process aim one should collect some data from the process itself. These data should be plotted on a control chart. If this has been done, then the control chart will provide a value for Sigma(X) to use in constructing the limits for the chart for Individual Values. In particular:

$$\text{Sigma(X)} = \frac{\overline{R}}{d_2}.$$

In the absence of any prior knowledge about the process, one will have to use the data as they are collected to determine both the process dispersion and the process average. Any failure to first determine the process dispersion will inevitably result in incorrect and inappropriate adjustments of the process aim. One simply cannot make an intelligent decision as to whether the process average is close to the target value without some measure of process dispersion. One way of doing this is shown in the procedure below:

M1. The central line for the X chart will be set at the target value. From 5 to 10 Individual values will be obtained and plotted in a running record against this central line. (If eight or more successive values are all on one side of the target, skip to Step M7 below.)

M2. The Moving Ranges for these 5 to 10 Individual Values are computed and plotted on a Moving Range Chart. The Average Moving Range is found and used to compute a value for Sigma(X):

$$\frac{\overline{mR}}{1.128} = \text{Sigma(X)}.$$

M3. The computed Sigma(X) value for Individual Values will be used to establish the three-sigma limits on either side of the central line on the X-Chart.

M4. One-sigma and two-sigma lines will be drawn, centered on the central line, on both sides of the chart for Individual Values.

M5. The initial 5 to 10 values will be examined for evidence of a lack of control relative to these limits using Detection Rules I, II, III, and IV. If any evidence of a lack of control is found, the process aim will need to be adjusted. Skip to Step M7 below.

M6. If the initial values fail to detect a lack of control, additional values may be collected. As each new point is plotted, Detection Rules I, II, III, and IV will be used to examine the data for a lack of control. Any lack of control on the Individual Chart will represent an off-target process.

M7. When a lack of control is detected, the average of the observations will provide a reasonable estimate of where the process average is located relative to the target, and the process aim should be adjusted accordingly. Following each adjustment of the process aim, return to Step M6 above.

M8. When 10 successive measurements fail to indicate a lack of control, using all four detection rules, the process average is said to be reasonably close to the target. At this point one may shift from the "aim setting mode" back to a "monitoring mode" where the control chart tracks the process for potential upsets.

While the Sigma(X) value found in the procedure above may not be based upon very much data, it will still be better than guesswork, especially when needless adjustments can result in excess nonconforming product. Yes, one wants to react as soon as possible. Yes, one cannot afford to wait too long before making a needed adjustment. But how will one know when it is needed?

It will always be a mistake to adjust the process aim before one has a detectable signal that the process average is off-target.

The control chart provides (among other things) an operational definition of when the process aim needs to be adjusted. Children yank the steering wheel back and forth when they play like they are driving. Drivers adjust the steering only when they want to change course, *or when they have a signal* that they are headed in the wrong direction. One does not have to weave back and forth to prove that one is not asleep at the wheel. When timeliness of adjustment is important, then one should collect the measurements as quickly as possible. In the absence of a prior value for Sigma(X), one will have to collect some data before even attempting to adjust the process aim. Of course, in the absence of a control chart for a given process, one may try to adjust the aim of an out-of-control process—generally an exercise in frustration—but if such is necessary, the steps above are the best way of attempting to do this.

Many years ago Grubbs published a procedure for setting the process aim which does not require a value for Sigma(X).[*] While Grubbs' Rule is fairly simple, it is essentially a modified form of tampering. This is because it has one adjust the process aim without first attempting to filter out the noise.

Grubbs' Rule can take a process which is on-target and move it off-target. Thus, like all procedures that do not take the natural variation in the numbers into account, it is capable of misleading the user. With Grubbs' Rule the operator will start making adjustments after the first measurement, and will continue to make adjustments following each additional measurement for some finite period of time. While this may give the illusion of action, the actions may well be the wrong actions.

So, even though one may chafe at having to collect 5 to 10 values without readjusting the process aim, it is the only prudent course of action. It will always be folly to make adjustments in the absence of a signal indicating that an adjustment is needed.

---

[*] Frank E. Grubbs, "An Optimum Procedure for Setting Machines or Adjusting Processes," **Journal of Quality Technology**, V.15, No.4, October 1983, pp.186-189, reprinted from the July 1954 issue of **Industrial Quality Control**.

Chapter Ten

Setting the Process Aim
Using Difference Charts

The control chart gives a lot of information about the process average. As was seen in the previous chapter, the chart for Individual Values may be used to help set the process aim. Yet this introduction of a special control chart for setting the process aim may be unnecessary.

In a short run environment one is likely to already be using a Difference Chart for Individual Values, or a Zed Chart. If the Nominal value used with these charts is the target value, then any out-of-control condition on the chart for location will indicate that the process average is off-target, and the process aim is in need of adjustment.

Thus, when short production runs call for frequent changes in the process aim, the Difference Chart or the Zed Chart can be used to check on the appropriateness of the adjustments. Say, for example, the target has just changed from 24 to 35. Then, in response to this change in the target value the operator will make certain changes in the process aim. Following this adjustment of the process aim, use the new target value to obtain the Difference Values for each new measurement. Whenever these Difference Values indicate a lack of control, the process aim will need further adjustment.

Notice the nature of the decision outlined above. The operator has made a deliberate adjustment in the process aim. The question is not whether or not the operator made an adjustment, but rather if the adjustment achieved the desired result. The Difference Value, or the Zed Value, will be computed under the assumption that the adjustment produced the desired effect. An out of control signal will suggest otherwise. Since we will want to know as soon as possible if the process average is not reasonably close to the target value, we will typically increase the sensitivity of the control chart in the "aim setting mode" by (1) using

Detection Rules I, II, III and IV and (2) increasing the sample frequency. This need for increased sensitivity will be greatest when the process is not capable, or is just barely capable of meeting specifications.

The use of these four detection rules will always be much better than simply tightening the control limits. Tightening the control limits will always increase the chances of a false alarm. When setting the process aim, these false alarms will result in needless adjustments, giving potential increases in nonconforming product. On the other hand, the four detection rules given earlier will increase the sensitivity of the control chart without greatly changing the likelihood of false alarms.[*]

Whenever ten successive values following an adjustment of the process aim fail to indicate a lack of control, using all four detection rules, one may conclude that the process average is reasonably close to the target value. At this point one could shift from an "aim setting mode" into a monitoring mode, at least until the next change in the target value comes along. In the monitoring mode, one may sample the process less often than is done in the "aim setting mode."

This procedure has the advantage of using an existing control chart. One simply shifts into high gear when evaluating a known change in the process aim, and shifts back when satisfied that the process average is reasonably close to the target value. The feature which makes this simple procedure work is the fact that both the Difference Chart and the Zed Chart are already set up to accommodate a target value.

In short, when a known change is made in the process aim, adjust the data according to the desired change and examine the control charts closely to see if there is any evidence that the adjustment in the process aim failed to move the process average to the neighborhood of the target value. The closeness of this examination depends upon the Detection Rules used and the sample frequency. By increasing both the Detection Rules and the sample frequency, one makes the chart more sensitive. Once this increased sensitivity is unnecessary, one may return to a less intense monitoring mode with the control chart.

---

[*] For a fuller explanation of this phenomenon see the manuscript by the author entitled *"Contra* Two Sigma."

Chapter Eleven

Setting the Process Aim
Using Multiple Measurements

The procedures in the preceding chapters describe how to use a sequence of single measurements to set the process aim. When the measurements are obtained in a sequence, a sequential procedure such as a control chart is the best procedure to use. However, in those situations where several parts may be obtained and measured in a very short time, it may be more advantageous to use one of the specialized procedures in this chapter.

The Necessity of Process Stability

The whole procedure of setting the process aim will be futile if the process itself is not in control. If the process is not in control, then there is not one process average, but many. Or there is not one process standard deviation, but many. In short, no process exists as a well-defined entity unless it is in statistical control. Trying to set the aim of an unstable process is simply wasted effort. When a process is known to be unstable, one should work to identify and remove the assignable causes of this instability rather than waste time continually tweaking the controls.

While the procedures above used a control chart, and thus had a built-in check for process stability, the following procedure is a separate procedure which does not automatically check for process stability. Therefore, one should not attempt to use the following procedure on a process that is not being tracked by a control chart. Moreover, this chart should have the ranges in control, and any averages which are out of control should correspond to known adjustments of the process. If this is not the case, then one must identify and remove the assignable causes of the uncontrolled variation before proceeding further.

The Basic Procedure With Multiple Measurements

The basic procedure for adjusting the process aim is very simple:

1. Set the process aim.

2. Measure the specified number of pieces, n, and calculate the average.

3. If the average is NOT within some critical distance, D, of the target, then return to Step 1 above.

4. Proceed with the production run when the average of n measurements is less than D units away from the target.

Once he has been given consistent values for n and D, an operator can use this procedure to set the process average as close to the nominal aim as is necessary, and he can do it quickly and efficiently. Moreover, as long as he continues to use this procedure, both the operator and his supervisor can be confident that the process aim is being set correctly.

The Average Taguchi Loss

How then does the supervisor provide the operator with the values for n and D? Since one must have a decision rule that is appropriate for the amount of data available, one cannot arbitrarily choose values for n and D. The plans given below combine values of n and D that work.

Even with the following plans, there is still the problem of which plan to use. The process average will, in general, end up closer to the target when more data are used. Just how close does one need to be to the target? This is the question that be answered in practice. But how does one decide on a "degree of closeness?" Isn't perfection the target? As was observed in Chapter Eleven, we can never get the process average to exactly coincide with the target, so we must learn to live with "close enough." Thus, we need a measure of closeness. A way to do this was provided by Dr. Genichi Taguchi when he introduced his concept of a Loss Function.

Based on a quadratic approximation to the loss function in the neighborhood of the target value, the Average Loss Per Unit of Production will be proportional to the Mean Square Deviation About Target:

$$MSD(\tau) = \{ \, [Sigma(X)]^2 + [\, process\ average - target\,]^2 \, \}$$

For any given process, the best that one can do (short of modifying the process) is to have the process in a state of statistical control and perfectly centered on the target. As the process average deviates from the target, the $MSD(\tau)$ value will increase. When a plan for setting the process aim does a good job of getting the process average close to the target, it will have a small $MSD(\tau)$ value.

Thus, each time one of the following plans is used to set the process aim, the process average will end up somewhere (hopefully close to the target), and there will be a single $MSD(\tau)$ value. If these $MSD(\tau)$ values for a given plan are averaged, then this Average $MSD(\tau)$ value may be used to characterize this plan for setting the process aim. This Average $MSD(\tau)$ value for a given plan will be called the Average Taguchi Loss. These Average Taguchi Loss values will be expressed as percentages of the minimum loss (that loss which occurs when the process average is equal to the target). For a procedure to get an Average Taguchi Loss of 100% it would have to set the process average equal to the target value every time without error.

Plans for Setting the Process Aim

The key to an effective procedure for setting the process aim is the relationship between the amount of data collected and the decision rule used to interpret these data. If the amount of data is appropriate for the decision rule used, the decisions will tend to be correct most of the time. If the decision rule and the amount of data are mismatched, then the decisions will tend to be incorrect more often. Eight plans for setting the process aim are shown on the following pages. These eight plans match up the decision rule with the amount of data, so that one will generally get a process average that is reasonably close to the target value.

For the sake of generality, the distance between the process average and the target is expressed in Sigma(X) units (that is, it is written as some multiple of Sigma(X)). This means that in order to use these plans for setting the process aim, one must first compute a Sigma(X) value. The best place to obtain this Sigma(X) value is from a control chart for the product or process.

PLAN A: If one wants the process average to be within 2.88 Sigma(X) units of the target, use $n = 1$ and $D = 1.44$ Sigma(X). The Average Taguchi Loss for this plan is estimated to be less than 495% of minimum.

PLAN B: If one wants the process average to be within 2.0 Sigma(X) units of the target, use $n = 3$ and $D = 1.0$ Sigma(X). The Average Taguchi Loss for this plan is estimated to be less than 260% of minimum.

PLAN C: If one wants the process average to be within 1.5 Sigma(X) units of the target, use $n = 5$ and $D = 0.75$ Sigma(X). The Average Taguchi Loss for this plan is estimated to be less than 190% of minimum.

PLAN D: If one wants the process average to be within 1.0 Sigma(X) units of the target, use $n = 10$ and $D = 0.5$ Sigma(X). The Average Taguchi Loss for this plan is estimated to be less than 140% of minimum.

PLAN E: If one wants the process average to be within 0.75 Sigma(X) units of the target, use $n = 15$ and $D = 0.37$ Sigma(X). The Average Taguchi Loss for this plan is estimated to be less than 129% of minimum.

PLAN F: If one wants the process average to be within 0.5 Sigma(X) units of the target, use $n = 25$ and $D = 0.25$ Sigma(X). The Average Taguchi Loss for this plan is estimated to be less than 114% of minimum.

PLAN G: If one wants the process average to be within 0.33 Sigma(X) units of the target, use $n = 40$ and $D = 0.17$ Sigma(X). The Average Taguchi Loss for this plan is estimated to be less than 110% of minimum.

PLAN H: If one wants the process average to be within 0.20 Sigma(X) units of the target, use $n = 71$ and $D = 0.10$ Sigma(X). The Average Taguchi Loss for this plan is estimated to be less than 103% of minimum.

Plans for Setting the Process Aim

Plan	Number of Measurements	Critical Distance D	Average Taguchi Loss
A	1	1.44 Sigma(X)	495%
B	3	1.00 Sigma(X)	260%
C	5	0.75 Sigma(X)	190%
D	10	0.50 Sigma(X)	140%
E	15	0.37 Sigma(X)	129%
F	25	0.25 Sigma(X)	114%
G	40	0.17 Sigma(X)	110%
H	71	0.10 Sigma(X)	103%

These adjustment procedures will be adequate for most of the routine adjustment problems where multiple measurements may be easily obtained. By choosing a plan further down the list, the process average will be set closer to the target. Of course, this in turn, requires more measurements.

Figure 22 shows the Average Taguchi Loss for each plan, and the Number of Measurements required by each plan.

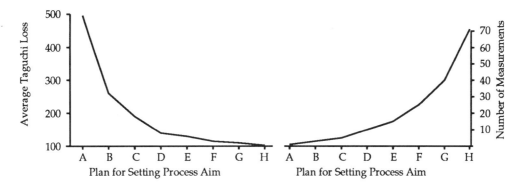

**Figure 22: Average Taguchi Loss and Number of Measurements
for Plans for Setting the Process Aim**

If the cost of variation from target is high relative to the cost of collecting the measurements and adjusting the process aim, then the situation in Figure 23 will hold. Here Plans D, E, and F appear to be reasonable.

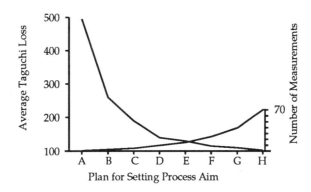

Figure 23: Large Cost of Variation and Small Cost of Measurements

If the cost of variation from target is small relative to the cost of collecting the measurements and adjusting the process aim, then the situation in Figure 24 will hold. In this case it is Plans B, C, and D that appear to be reasonable.

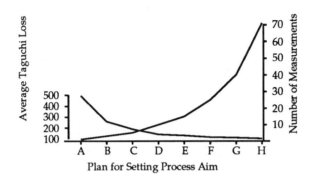

Figure 24: Small Cost of Variation and Large Cost of Measurements

If one is not certain just what the costs of variation are relative to the cost of collecting the measurements and adjusting the process aim, the two graphs above suggest that Plan D is reasonable in any case.

A sample worksheet for using these plans to adjust the process aim is shown in Figure 25. The information shown on this worksheet will greatly simplify the actual decision-making process on the production floor.

Using Single Values to Set the Process Aim

If the nature of the process, or the nature of the measurement, dictates the use of single measurements in setting the process aim, then one will be limited in the ability to verify that the process average is close to the target. Plan A shows a value of $D = 1.44$ Sigma(X) for $n = 1$. This means that if one gets a single measurement within D units of the target, it is very likely that the process average is within $2D$ units of the target.

Using a smaller value for D will not deliver any greater certainty. With only one measurement there is only a limited amount of information available, and nothing can change this limitation. The only real consequence of using a smaller value for D would be an increased number of needless adjustments.

If one can use a sequence of single measurements, then rather than repeatedly using Plan A, it is generally better to use the Individual Values Chart described in Chapter 12.

Date _____ Part Number _____ Operator _____

Process or Machine _____ other ID _____

Dimension Measured _____ Target Value _____

Sigma(X) Value _____ Plan Used _____

Sample Size n = _____ Critical Distance D = _____

Adjust Process Aim if Average of n Measurements is Outside Decision Interval:

Decision Interval: Target $- D$ = _____ Target $+ D$ = _____

	First Sample Measurements	Second Sample Measurements	Third Sample Measurements	Plan	n	D
1	_____	_____	_____			
2	_____	_____	_____	A	1	1.44 Sigma(X)
3	_____	_____	_____	B	3	1.00 Sigma(X)
4	_____	_____	_____	C	5	0.75 Sigma(X)
5	_____	_____	_____	D	10	0.50 Sigma(X)
6	_____	_____	_____	E	15	0.37 Sigma(X)
7	_____	_____	_____	F	25	0.25 Sigma(X)
8	_____	_____	_____	G	40	0.17 Sigma(X)
9	_____	_____	_____	H	71	0.10 Sigma(X)
10	_____	_____	_____			
11	_____	_____	_____			
12	_____	_____	_____			
13	_____	_____	_____			
14	_____	_____	_____			
15	_____	_____	_____			

Average _____ _____ _____

Decision _____ _____ _____

Figure 25: Worksheet for Setting the Process Aim

Chapter Twelve

World-Class Quality

For almost 200 years quality was defined by conformance to specifications. As long as the product characteristics fell within the specified range, the product was deemed "suitable for its intended purpose" and a "loss" of zero was assigned to that unit. However, as soon as some product characteristic strayed outside the specification limits there was a definite and non-zero "loss" attached to that unit. This loss includes the cost of (1) reworking the product (or scrapping it), (2) the cost of investigating the problem and attempting to "fix the process," (3) the cost of getting the production line stabilized after all of the "adjustments" have been made, and (4) the time and energy spent in writing the memos and reports necessary to document the actions taken. Thus, defining quality as conformance to specifications resulted in a step-function model for the losses due to variation.

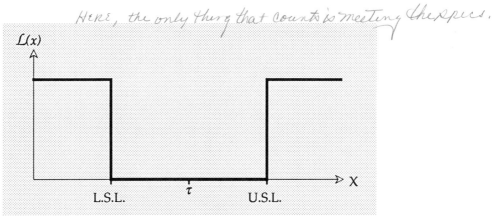

HERE, the only thing that counts is meeting the specs.

Figure 26: Loss Function for Conformance to Specifications Definition of Quality

This step-function view of the losses due to variation has an inevitable consequence. It will always result in periods of benign neglect broken by periods of total panic and chaos. As long as the product conforms to the specifications the loss is thought to be zero, and nothing is done. As soon as the product is nonconforming, the demand for action will create panic and chaos. In such an environment, continual improvement will be impossible—the discipline and constancy of purpose required will always be missing.

World Class Quality was redefined over 30 years ago by Dr. Taguchi's Quadratic Loss Function. Instead of a step-function, with zero loss throughout the specification range, he argued that a more realistic model would be some convex curve, with minimum at the target value.

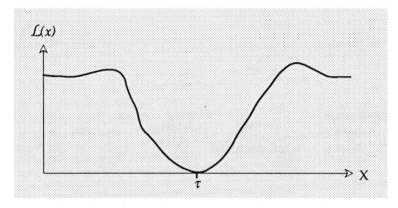

Figure 27: A More Realistic Loss Function

Once this new view of the losses associated with variation about a target value is adopted, certain results follow. If the curve in Figure 14.2 is piecewise smooth, non-negative, and zero at the target, it may be approximated by a Taylor series expansion in some region near the target. When this is done, the first non-zero term in the expansion will be the term involving the square of the difference between the individual value and the target. Using this single term, a first order approximation to the convex loss function, in the neighborhood of the target value, will be:

$$L(x) \approx K(x-\tau)^2$$

As the value for x changes for each item produced, the loss function will vary. If the production process displays statistical control, one can meaningfully discuss the product distribution. Say that the probability model $f(x)$ approximates this product distribution. Then, using the quadratic approximation shown above, the Average Loss Per Unit of Production will be:

$$E\{L(x)\} = \int L(x) f(x)\, dx = K\{\sigma^2 + (\mu-\tau)^2\}$$

where σ is the standard deviation of the *stable* production process, μ is the mean of the *stable* production process, and τ is the target value.

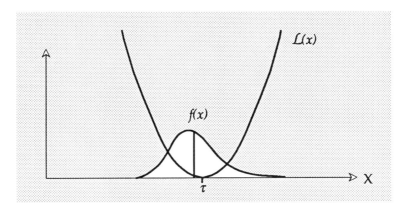

Figure 28: A Quadratic Loss Function with a Product Distribution

This result holds regardless of the form of $f(x)$. Therefore, the Average Loss Due to Variation Per Unit of Production depends upon the square of the process standard deviation and the square of the process bias. In order to minimize this average loss, one will need to minimize the variation of the process, and operate the process on target—hence the new definition of world class quality as "On Target with Minimum Variance."

On target with minimum variance is what it takes to *minimize the cost of variation.* Nothing else will do this. Any other approach to operations, such as conformance to specifications, will result in an increased cost of operation due to the increased costs of variation. This is theorem that cannot be evaded.

On target with minimum variance requires a process that is operated in a state of statistical control, and is properly set to operate at the correct level. The techniques in this book may be used to do just that.

IN PRACTICE:

EST. AVG. LOSS PER UNIT $= K \{ mSD (\tau) \}$

$$= K \{ (\bar{R}/d_2)^2 + (\bar{x} - \tau)^2 \}$$

This tracks "on target with minimum variance". It's different than C_p & C_{pk}.

To ESTIMATE K, Determine a deviation from τ which has a known cost, ex SCRAP OR REWORK.

$\mathcal{L}(x) = K (x - \tau)^2$

$C_{SCRAP} - K (x_{SCRAP} - \tau)^2$ & Solve for K

57

Table A
Bias Correction Factors
For Estimating Standard Deviations

Subgroup Size	d_2	c_2	c_4	d_3	Subgroup Size	d_2	c_2	c_4	d_3
2	1.128	0.5642	.7979	0.8525	21	3.778	0.9638	.9876	0.7272
3	1.693	0.7236	.8862	0.8884	22	3.819	0.9655	.9882	0.7199
4	2.059	0.7979	.9213	0.8798	23	3.858	0.9670	.9887	0.7159
5	2.326	0.8407	.9400	0.8641	24	3.895	0.9684	.9892	0.7121
6	2.534	0.8686	.9515	0.8480	25	3.931	0.9695	.9896	0.7084
7	2.704	0.8882	.9594	0.8332	30	4.086	0.9748	.9915	0.6927
8	2.847	0.9027	.9650	0.8198	35	4.213	0.9784	.9927	0.6799
9	2.970	0.9139	.9693	0.8078	40	4.322	0.9811	.9936	0.6692
10	3.078	0.9227	.9727	0.7971	45	4.415	0.9832	.9943	0.6601
11	3.173	0.9300	.9754	0.7873	50	4.498	0.9849	.9949	0.6521
12	3.258	0.9359	.9776	0.7785	60	4.639	0.9874	.9957	0.6389
13	3.336	0.9410	.9794	0.7704	70	4.755	0.9892	.9963	0.6283
14	3.407	0.9453	.9810	0.7630	80	4.854	0.9906	.9968	0.6194
15	3.472	0.9490	.9823	0.7562	90	4.939	0.9916	.9972	0.6118
16	3.532	0.9523	.9835	0.7499	100	5.015	0.9925	.9975	0.6052
17	3.588	0.9551	.9845	0.7441					
18	3.640	0.9576	.9854	0.7386					
19	3.689	0.9599	.9862	0.7335					
20	3.735	0.9619	.9869	0.7287					

Sigma(X) and Sigma(R) values may be obtained from any of the following:

$$\text{Sigma(X) is } \quad \frac{\bar{s}_n}{c_2} \quad \text{ or } \quad \frac{\bar{s}}{c_4} \quad \text{ or } \quad \frac{\bar{R}}{d_2} \quad \text{ or } \quad \frac{\overline{mR}}{d_2}$$

$$\text{Sigma(R) is } \frac{d_3 \bar{R}}{d_2}$$

Table B
Control Chart Factors

For any number of subgroups
of size n with

Grand Average, $\bar{\bar{X}}$, or Grand Average, $\bar{\bar{X}}$,

Average Range, $\bar{R}$, Average Standard Deviation, $\bar{s}$

Subgroup Size n	A_2	D_3	D_4	Subgroup Size n	A_3	B_3	B_4
2	1.880	--	3.268	2	2.659	--	3.267
3	1.023	--	2.574	3	1.954	--	2.568
4	0.729	--	2.282	4	1.628	--	2.266
5	0.577	--	2.114	5	1.427	--	2.089
6	0.483	--	2.004	6	1.287	0.030	1.970
7	0.419	0.076	1.924	7	1.182	0.118	1.882
8	0.373	0.136	1.864	8	1.099	0.185	1.815
9	0.337	0.184	1.816	9	1.032	0.239	1.761
10	0.308	0.223	1.777	10	0.975	0.284	1.716

$$UCL_{\bar{x}} = \bar{\bar{X}} + A_2 \bar{R} \qquad\qquad UCL_{\bar{x}} = \bar{\bar{X}} + A_3 \bar{s}$$

$$CL_{\bar{x}} = \bar{\bar{X}} \qquad\qquad CL_{\bar{x}} = \bar{\bar{X}}$$

$$LCL_{\bar{x}} = \bar{\bar{X}} - A_2 \bar{R} \qquad\qquad LCL_{\bar{x}} = \bar{\bar{X}} - A_3 \bar{s}$$

$$UCL_R = D_4 \bar{R} \qquad\qquad UCL_s = B_4 \bar{s}$$

$$CL_R = \bar{R} \qquad\qquad CL_s = \bar{s}$$

$$LCL_R = D_3 \bar{R} \qquad\qquad LCL_s = B_3 \bar{s}$$

And for $n > 10$:

$$A_2 = \frac{3}{d_2 \sqrt{n}} \qquad\qquad A_3 = \frac{3}{c_4 \sqrt{n}}$$

$$D_3 = [\, 1 - \frac{3 d_3}{d_2} \,] \qquad\qquad B_3 = [\, 1 - \frac{3}{\sqrt{2(n-1)}} \,]$$

$$D_4 = [\, 1 + \frac{3 d_3}{d_2} \,] \qquad\qquad B_4 = [\, 1 + \frac{3}{\sqrt{2(n-1)}} \,]$$

Glossary

A_2	a control chart constant, p.22, Table B.
Average Taguchi Loss	the average MSD(t) value for a given plan, p.48.
CL_R	Central Line for a Range Chart, p.6.
d_2	a control chart constant, p.9,10, Table A.
d_3	a control chart constant, p.9,10, Table A.
D	the critical distance for decision rules for setting the process aim, p.48.
D_3	a control chart constant, p.22, Table B.
D_4	a control chart constant, p.22, Table B.
H	the multiplier for finding limits for charts for Mean Ranges, p.9.
k	the number of subgroups in a collection of subgroups, p.9.
K	the constant which converts MSD(τ) into cost of variation from target, p.56.
$L(x)$	the loss for a given value of some product quality characteristic, p.55.
m	the number of Subgroup Ranges averaged to obtain one of a set of Average Ranges, p.9.
mR	a Moving Range value, the difference of two successive values, p.4.
MSD(τ)	the Mean Squared Deviation About Target, p.49.
n	the subgroup size, p.9, and the amount of data used in setting the process aim, p.48.
Nominal	a "named" value, p.5.
$\bar{R}$	the Average Range for a set of k Ranges, p.12.
$\bar{\bar{R}}$	the Overall Average Range for a set of m Average Ranges, p.9.
Sigma(X)	a value used to characterize dispersion for a set of data, p.11, Table A.
Sigma($\bar{X}$)	a value used to characterize dispersion for a set of subgroup averages, p.27.
τ	the target value for a product quality characteristic, p.56.
UCL_R	Upper Control Limit for a Range Chart, p.6.
UCL_W	Upper Control Limit for a standardized Range Chart, p.13.
W	a standardized range value, p.13.

Glossary
(continued)

W^* a quasi-standardized range value, p.15.

$\bar{W}$ an average standardized range value, p.19.

X   an individual measurement, p.4.

$\bar{X}$ a subgroup average value, p.21.

XmR   Chart for Individual Values and a Moving Range, p.4.

Z   a standardized individual measurement value, p.12.

Z^* a quasi-standardized individual measurement value, p.15.

$\bar{Z}$ a standardized subgroup average value, p.27.

$\bar{Z}^*$ a quasi-standardized subgroup average value, p.27.